Sid's Pet Rat

Written by Jeanne Willis

Illustrated by Jess Mikhail

Before and during reading

❶ Say the sounds

ck	e	u	r

❷ Blend the sounds

pet	rat	sun	muck
get	rid	deck	

❸ Read the tricky words

the	no	go

Point out the tricky bit of the word (i.e. the 'e' in 'the' sounds /u/) and then blend the rest.

Story comprehension

Read the title and look at the cover. Has your child read about Sid before? Who else might this story be about?

Vocabulary check

Turn to page 9 to discuss the meaning of 'rid'.

Reading the story

- Listen to your child reading the story. Ask them to blend words they do not recognise immediately.
- Ask them to read the text at the bottom of the page before they read the speech bubble on page 7.
- Check they recognise the lady on page 7.
- On page 9, check they understand who Nan is talking *to* and who she is talking *about*.
- On page 10, ask your child what they think might happen next.

Dots and dashes? The dots show one sound made by one letter. The dashes show one sound made by two letters.

Sid's Pet Rat

Written by Jeanne Willis

Illustrated by Jess Mikhail

Sid's pet rat

Rat sat in the sun.

Rat sat in the muck.

Rat sat on the deck.

Nan sat on Rat!

After reading

Story comprehension

- Ask your child to explain what happened in the story.
- Does Nan like Rat? How do you know?
- What clues are there in the pictures on pages 10–11 that Nan was sitting there?

Picture detective

Ask your child to find the object in the picture that contains the:

/u/ sound (page 6 – bug)

/ck/ sound (page 11 – ro<u>ck</u>)

Remember to prompt and praise!

Follow up

Speedy reading

Return to the words on the front inside cover (sections 2 and 3) and check your child can sound out and blend these words confidently. Ask them to practise blending them until they can read them quickly.

Segmenting for spelling

Practise this spelling routine using the words in section 2.

- Say the word in a sentence, then on its own and ask your child to repeat it.
- Encourage your child to say the sounds all through the word (segment) and either write a dash or hold up a finger for each sound.
- They then select magnetic letters or write down the letter for each sound, saying the sound quietly as they do so.
- Model the spelling by saying each sound as you write the word for your child to see.
- Give your child a tick for each letter in the correct place.

Published by Pearson Education Limited, 80 Strand, London, WC2R 0RL.

www.pearsonschools.co.uk

Text © Pearson Education Limited 2010

Original illustrations © Harcourt Education Limited 2007

Illustrated by Jess Mikhail

Designed by Bigtop

First published 2010

This edition published 2020

20 19 18 17 16

10 9 8 7 6 5 4 3 2 1

British Library Cataloguing in Publication Data

A catalogue record for this book is available from the British Library

Note from the publisher

Pearson has robust editorial processes, including answer and fact checks, to ensure the accuracy of the content in this publication, and every effort is made to ensure this publication is free of errors. We are, however, only human, and occasionally errors do occur. Pearson is not liable for any misunderstandings that arise as a result of errors in this publication, but it is our priority to ensure that the content is accurate. If you spot an error, please do contact us at resourcescorrections@pearson.com so we can make sure it is corrected.

Sid and Duck

Written by Emma Lynch

Illustrated by Jess Mikhail

Before and during reading

1 **Say the sounds**

ck	e	u	r

2 **Blend the sounds**

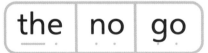

Duck	gets	cup
up	suds	rug

3 **Read the tricky words**

the	no	go

Point out the tricky bit of the word (i.e. the 'e' in 'the' sounds /u/) and then blend the rest.

Story comprehension

Read the title. Has your child read any of the other stories with Sid in? If not, introduce the character of Sid and explain that he often gets up to mischief. Have a look at the pictures of him inside. What do they think this story might be about?

Vocabulary check

Check that your child understands the meaning of the following words: dip, suds. Where would you find 'suds'? What would make the 'suds'?

Reading the story

● Listen to your child reading the story. Ask them to say the sounds and blend them in order to read words they do not recognise immediately.

● On page 23, point out that there are speech bubbles on the page. What does this show us? Remind your child to read the words in speech bubbles as expressively as they can to show how the character might speak.

Dots and dashes? The dots show one sound made by one letter. The dashes show one sound made by two letters.

Sid and Duck

Written by Emma Lynch
Illustrated by Jess Mikhail

Duck is on the tap.

Sid gets in.

Sid dips Duck.
Sid ducks Duck.

Duck is mad at Sid.

The cup tips up.
Suds go on the rug.

After reading

Story comprehension

- On page 20, what does Sid do to Duck? Is Duck happy about it? How does your child know?
- What happens to the cup on page 22?
- Who does Sid blame for the mess on the rug? Does Nan believe him?
- Look at page 8. Why is Duck winking?

Picture detective

Ask your child to find the object in the picture that contains the:

/ck/ sound (pages 19, 22 and 23 – so<u>ck</u>)

/r/ sound (pages 18, 19, 20, 22, and 23 – <u>R</u>at, in the picture frame)

Remember to prompt and praise!

Follow up

Speedy reading

Return to the words on the front inside cover (sections 2 and 3) and check your child can sound out and blend these words confidently. Ask them to practise blending them until they can read them quickly.

Segmenting for spelling

Practise this spelling routine using the words in section 2.

- Say the word in a sentence, then on its own and ask your child to repeat it.
- Encourage your child to say the sounds all through the word (segment) and either write a dash or hold up a finger for each sound.
- They then select magnetic letters or write down the letter for each sound, saying the sound quietly as they do so.
- Model the spelling by saying each sound as you write the word for your child to see.
- Give your child a tick for each letter in the correct place.

Published by Pearson Education Limited, 80 Strand, London, WC2R 0RL.

www.pearsonschools.co.uk

Text © Pearson Education Limited 2010

Original illustrations © Pearson Education Limited 2009

Illustrated by Jess Mikhail

Designed by Bigtop

First published 2010
This edition published 2020

20 19 18 17 16
10 9 8 7 6 5 4 3 2 1

British Library Cataloguing in Publication Data
A catalogue record for this book is available from the British Library

The Bop

Written by Jeanne Willis

Illustrated by Lee Wildish

Before and during reading

① Say the sounds

h	b	f	ff	l	ll

② Blend the sounds

let's	fun	bus	bat
bop	hen	hop	cub
sal/sa	bug	puff	bob

Dots and dashes? The dots show one sound made by one letter. The dashes show one sound made by two letters.

③ Read the tricky words

I	in/to

Point out the tricky bit of the word (i.e. the 'o' in 'into' sounds /oo/) and then blend the rest.

Story comprehension

Read the title of the book. What is a 'bop'?

Vocabulary check

Turn to pages 34–35. What do the words 'rock' and 'rap' mean? Explain that 'salsa' is another kind of dance.

Point out if necessary that each of the animals is referred to by their animal name (e.g. bat, hen, cub, bug) and their given name, which is shown by the use of the capital letter at the beginning of the word, for example, 'Hop, Hen, hop!'. Explain that in this story the characters' animal name and given name is the same.

Reading the story

● Listen to your child reading the story. Ask them to say the sounds and blend them in order to read any words they do not recognise immediately.

● On page 30, ask your child what they think might happen on a fun bus.

● Remind your child to read the text at the bottom of the page before they read the speech bubbles on pages 33 and 36.

The Bop

Written by Jeanne Willis
Illustrated by Lee Wildish

Let's get into the fun bus.

Go to the bop!

The bat can bob.
Bob, bob, bob!

The hen can hop.
Hop, Hen, hop!

The cub can rock.
Rock it, Cub!

The bug can rap.
Rap, Bug, rap!

I can salsa!

After reading

Story comprehension

- Can your child recall any of the things the characters did in the story?
- Re-read the speech bubble on page 36. Why are they puffing at the end?

Picture detective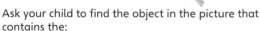

Ask your child to find the object in the picture that contains the:

/b/ sound (page 34 – bell)

/h/ sound (page 35 – hat)

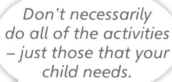

Don't necessarily do all of the activities – just those that your child needs.

Follow up

Speedy reading

Return to the words on the front inside cover (sections 2 and 3) and check your child can sound out and blend these words confidently. Ask them to practise blending them until they can read them quickly.

Segmenting for spelling

Practise this spelling routine using the words in section 2.

- Say the word in a sentence, then on its own and ask your child to repeat it.
- Encourage your child to say the sounds all through the word (segment) and either write a dash or hold up a finger for each sound.
- They then select magnetic letters or write down the letter for each sound, saying the sound quietly as they do so.
- Model the spelling by saying each sound as you write the word for your child to see.
- Give your child a tick for each letter in the correct place.

Published by Pearson Education Limited, 80 Strand, London, WC2R 0RL.

www.pearsonschools.co.uk

Text © Pearson Education Limited 2010

Original illustrations © Harcourt Education Limited 2007

Illustrated by Lee Wildish

Designed by Bigtop

First published 2010
This edition published 2020

20 19 18 17 16
10 9 8 7 6 5 4 3 2 1

British Library Cataloguing in Publication Data
A catalogue record for this book is available from the British Library

Note from the publisher
Pearson has robust editorial processes, including answer and fact checks, to ensure the accuracy of the content in this publication, and every effort is made to ensure this publication is free of errors. We are, however, only human, and occasionally errors do occur. Pearson is not liable for any misunderstandings that arise as a result of use of this publication, but it is our priority to ensure that the content is accurate. If you spot an error, please do contact us at resourcescorrections@pearson.com so we can make sure it is corrected.

Big Fat Rat

Written by Nicola Sandford

Illustrated by Jess Mikhail

Before and during reading

① Say the sounds

h	b	f	ff	l	ll	ss

② Blend the sounds

hops	off	licks
less	bobs	bet
ill	bed	but
big	fat	

③ Read the tricky words

I	in/to

Point out the tricky bit of the word (i.e. the 'o' in 'into' sounds /oo/) and then blend the rest.

Story comprehension

Read the title and look at the picture on the cover. Who does your child think the story is going to be about? What might a 'big fat rat' do?

Vocabulary check

Check that your child understands what we mean by the following expressions: 'bobs up', 'tucks in'. What kind of sleep is a 'nap'? Also, ensure that your child understands that the phrase 'Less of it!' is a way of saying 'Don't do that!'

Reading the story

- Listen to your child reading the story. Ask them to say the sounds and blend them in order to read words they do not recognise immediately.
- Point out that there are speech marks on the pages 42 and 43. What does this show us? Remind your child to read the words in speech marks as expressively as they can to show how the character might speak. Who is speaking here?
- Stop on page 45 and ask your child to predict how they think the story will end.

Dots and dashes? The dots show one sound made by one letter. The dashes show one sound made by two letters.

Big Fat Rat

Written by Nicola Sandford
Illustrated by Jess Mikhail

Rat hops on.

"Get off it, Rat."

Rat licks it.
"Less of it, Rat!"

Rat hops off.
Rat bobs up.

Rat tucks in.

Rat naps.

"I bet Rat is ill."

"Get into bed, Rat."

But Rat is not ill.
"Big fat Rat!"

After reading

Story comprehension

- Why is Rat called 'big fat Rat'? What does he do?
- What happens on pages 44 and 45 when Rat 'hops off'? Ask your child to retell this part of the story, shown in the four circular pictures, in their own words.
- How does your child know that Rat is not ill at the end?
- Do they think that Sid and his sister are cross with Rat at the end or not? Why?

Picture detective

Ask your child to find the object in the picture that contains the:

/b/ sound (page 42 – <u>b</u>in)

/l/ sound (page 42 – <u>cl</u>ock) If necessary, give your child a hint that the /l/ sound has a /c/ sound in front of it.

Remember to prompt and praise!

Follow up

Speedy reading

Return to the words on the front inside cover (sections 2 and 3) and check your child can sound out and blend these words confidently. Ask them to practise blending them until they can read them quickly.

Segmenting for spelling

Practise this spelling routine using the words in section 2.

- Say the word in a sentence, then on its own and ask your child to repeat it.
- Encourage your child to say the sounds all through the word (segment) and either write a dash or hold up a finger for each sound.
- They then select magnetic letters or write down the letter for each sound, saying the sound quietly as they do so.
- Model the spelling by saying each sound as you write the word for your child to see.
- Give your child a tick for each letter in the correct place.

Published by Pearson Education Limited, 80 Strand, London, WC2R 0RL.

www.pearsonschools.co.uk

Text © Pearson Education Limited 2010

Original illustrations © Pearson Education Limited 2009

Illustrated by Jess Mikhail

Designed by Bigtop

First published 2010

This edition published 2020

20 19 18 17 16

10 9 8 7 6 5 4 3 2 1

British Library Cataloguing in Publication Data

A catalogue record for this book is available from the British Library

Note from the publisher

Pearson has robust editorial processes, including answer and fact checks, to ensure the accuracy of the content in this publication, and every effort is made to ensure this publication is free of errors. We are, however, only human, and occasionally errors do occur. Pearson is not liable for any misunderstandings that arise as a result of errors in this publication, but it is our priority to ensure that the content is accurate. If you spot an error, please do contact us at resourcescorrections@pearson.com so we can make sure it is corrected.

Max's Box

Written by Monica Hughes
Illustrated by Sarah Horne

Before and during reading

① Say the sounds

j	v	w	x

② Blend the sounds

Max	box	Jan
twigs	wax	mix/es
cob/webs	six	jets
will	revs	swells
twin		

③ Read the tricky words

me	be

Point out the tricky bit of the word (i.e. the 'e' in 'me' and 'be' sounds /ee/) and then blend the rest.

Story comprehension

Read the title and introduce the main character – Max. Read page 54, 'Max is mad!', and talk about what silly things Max might do.

Vocabulary check

Check that your child understands what we mean by 'revs up'. Also, check their understanding of the following words: jets, swells, twin.

Reading the story

- Listen to your child reading the story. Ask them to say the sounds and blend them in order to read words they do not recognise immediately.
- Point out that there are speech bubbles on pages 56 and 57. Who is speaking here? How might Max say these words?
- Stop on page 65 and ask your child to predict what they think might happen to the box next.
- On page 66, point out the ellipsis (…). This shows us to pause and leads us on to what will happen next.
- Were your child's predictions correct?

Blending words with adjacent consonants?
t-w → tw-i-g-s → twigs, or
s-w → sw-e-ll-s → swells

Max's Box

Written by Monica Hughes

Illustrated by Sarah Horne

Max is mad!

Max drops the mix into the
big box.

Max mixes the cobwebs into the hot wax.

Max drops the mix into the big box.

Max gets six jets.

He revs up the jets.

The box begins to hiss.

The box begins to swell.

The box swells and ...

... up pops a Max twin!

After reading

Story comprehension

- What kind of person is Max? What kinds of things does he do?
- What things does Max put in his mix?
- What comes out of Max's box at the end? Is Max surprised?

Picture detective

Ask your child to find the object in the picture that contains the:

/x/ sound (page 55 – fo<u>x</u>)

/j/ sound (page 55 – <u>j</u>acket)

Remember to prompt and praise!

Follow up

Speedy reading

Return to the words on the front inside cover (sections 2 and 3) and check your child can sound out and blend these words confidently. Ask them to practise blending them until they can read them quickly.

Segmenting for spelling

Practise this spelling routine using the words in section 2.

- Say the word in a sentence, then on its own and ask your child to repeat it.
- Encourage your child to say the sounds all through the word (segment) and either write a dash or hold up a finger for each sound.
- They then select magnetic letters or write down the letter for each sound, saying the sound quietly as they do so.
- Model the spelling by saying each sound as you write the word for your child to see.
- Give your child a tick for each letter in the correct place.

Published by Pearson Education Limited, 80 Strand, London, WC2R 0RL.

www.pearsonschools.co.uk

Text © Pearson Education Limited 2010

Original illustrations © Pearson Education Limited 2009

Illustrated by Sarah Horne

Designed by Bigtop

First published 2010
This edition published 2020

20 19 18 17 16
10 9 8 7 6 5 4 3 2 1

British Library Cataloguing in Publication Data
A catalogue record for this book is available from the British Library

Note from the publisher
Pearson has robust editorial processes, including answer and fact checks, to ensure the accuracy of the content in this publication, and every effort is made to ensure this publication is free of errors. We are, however, only human, and occasionally errors do occur. Pearson is not liable for any misunderstandings that arise as a result of errors in this publication, but it is our priority to ensure that the content is accurate. If you spot an error, please do contact us at resourcescorrections@pearson.com so we can make sure it is corrected.

Go To Bed

Written by
Emma Lynch

Before and during reading

1 Say the sounds

j	v	w	x

2 Blend the sounds

Rex	Jon	twins
swop	six	Ti/va
wig/wam		box
just	job	Jess
well	Jip	

3 Read the tricky words

me	be

Point out the tricky bit of the word
(i.e. the 'e' in 'me' and 'be' sounds /ee/)
and then blend the rest.

Comprehension

Read the title and talk about what happens when your child goes to bed. Where do they sleep? What is their bed like? Have they ever slept somewhere different or unusual?

Vocabulary check

Check that your child understands the meaning of the word 'wigwam'. Do they know what a wigwam looks like? Do they know that there are different sorts of 'den'?

Reading the book

- Listen to your child reading the book. Ask them to say the sounds and blend them in order to read words they do not recognise immediately.
- On page 81, talk about what kind of 'bag' you might sleep in.
- On page 84, where is the foxes' den?

Blending words with adjacent consonants?
s-w → sw-o-p → swop, or
j-u-s-t → j-u-st → just

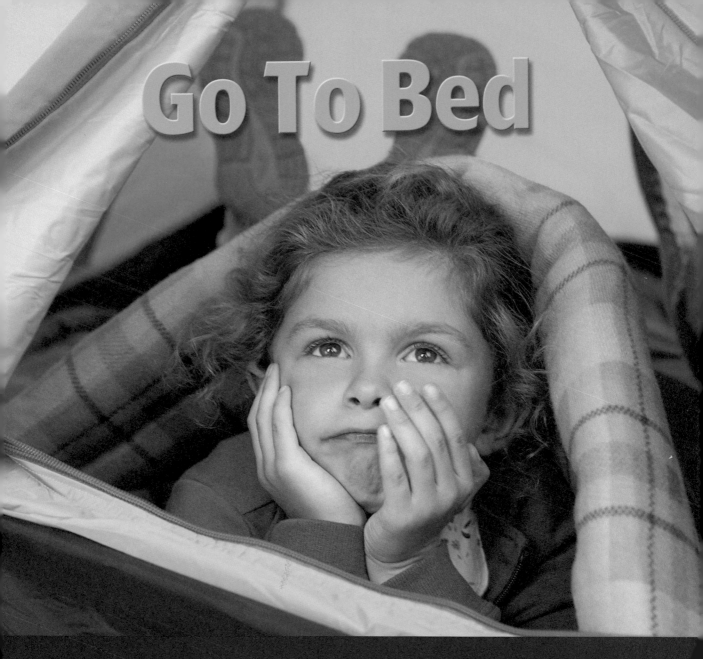

Go To Bed

Written by Emma Lynch

Let's go to bed.

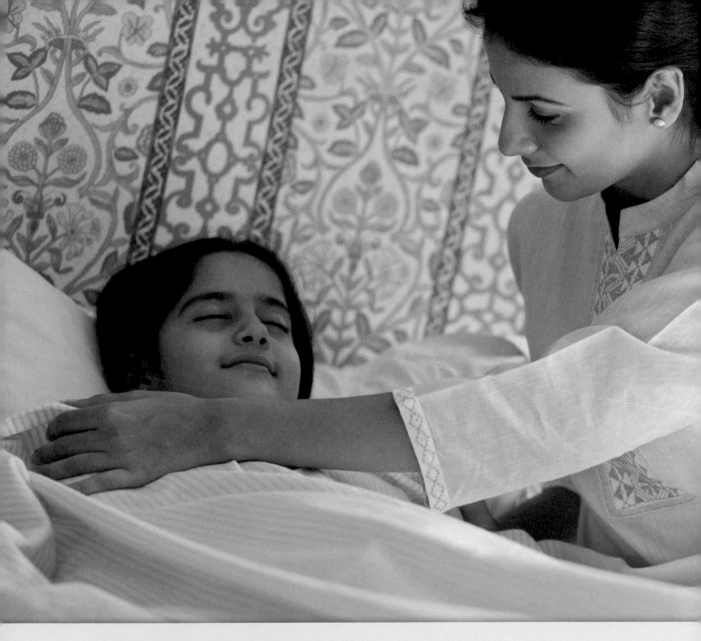

Mum tucks me up.

Rex naps on a rug.

Jon naps in his cot.

The twins can swop beds.

Mum's nest has six in a bed!

Tiva's bed is in a wigwam.

I go to bed in a bag!

A bed in a box can be snug.

I go to bed on a mat.

A bed in a den is just the job.

A bed in a den can be at the top!

Mum lets Jess nap with me.

I go to bed if I am not well.

Jip has not got a bed!